big

NATE

GAME ON!

big NATE

GAME ON!

by LINCOLN PEIRCE

SCHOLASTIC INC.

ISBN 978-0-545-63862-3

Big Nate: Game On! copyright © 2013 by United Feature Syndicate, Inc.
All rights reserved. Published by Scholastic Inc.,
557 Broadway, New York, NY 10012,
by arrangement with Andrews McMeel Publishing, LLC,
an Andrews McMeel Universal company.
SCHOLASTIC and associated logos are trademarks
and/or registered trademarks of Scholastic Inc.

12 11 10 9 8 7 6 5 4 3 2 1   13 14 15 16 17 18/0

Printed in the U.S.A.   40

First Scholastic printing, September 2013

HOLD IT! FOUL!

THAT'S A FOUL, NATE! IF YOU DO THAT IN A GAME, YOU'LL GET CALLED EVERY TIME!

WHAT? NO WAY!

I DIDN'T BUMP HIM, I DIDN'T GRAB HIM, I DIDN'T TRIP HIM!... TECHNICALLY, I DIDN'T EVEN **TOUCH HIS BODY!**

NEVERTHELESS...

MAY I GO TO THE LOCKER ROOM TO "ADJUST" MYSELF?

BIG GAME TODAY, MEN! THESE GUYS ARE UNDEFEATED. THIS'LL BE A TOUGH, TOUGH GAME.

THEY'RE TALLER, THEY'RE MORE SKILLED. BUT IF YOU HANG IN THERE, TRY TO STAY CLOSE... WELL, ANYTHING CAN HAPPEN!

DON'T OVERFOCUS ON THE FINAL OUTCOME. DO YOUR BEST, AND I'LL BE PROUD OF YOU NO MATTER WHAT!

CLAP CLAP CLAP

IF YOU'RE GOING TO MAKE ME PRACTICE FREE THROWS FOR AN HOUR A DAY, I MUST INSIST THAT YOU DO LIKEWISE WITH YOUR PRE-GAME PEP TALKS.

YOU LOOK LIKE **SHAQ** OUT THERE!

WELL, I WOULDN'T SAY **THAT**!

I MEAN... YES, I'VE BEEN DOMINANT, BUT I HAVEN'T BEEN **THAT** DOMINANT!

I WAS TALKING ABOUT YOUR **FREE THROW** SHOOTING!

...ALTHOUGH AT LEAST WHEN **SHAQ** SHOOTS FREE THROWS, HALF OF THEM GO **IN**!

THAT RIM'S TOO LOW. I **KNOW** IT.

THESE GUYS ARE REALLY SHUTTING DOWN OUR OFFENSE! ANY IDEAS, GUYS?

FEED ME.

I DON'T THINK SO, NATE. YOU'RE NOT TALL ENOUGH TO GO TO THE HOOP AGAINST THEIR BIG GUYS. WE NEED OTHER OPTIONS.

NO, I MEAN... **FEED** ME.

HE'S HUNGRY.

COME ON, WOULD IT BE ASKING TOO MUCH TO HAVE A FEW "HO-HO'S" ON THE BENCH?

"PSYCH-OUT" TIME!

WELL, WELL! NUMBER 23!

NUMBER 23 ON YOUR JERSEY... ON YOUR WRISTBAND... YOUR SOCKS... YOUR SNEAKERS...

TRYING TO "BE LIKE MIKE", HUH? THAT'S SAD, MAN.

SAD?

YEAH. SORT OF PATHETIC, Y'KNOW?

YOU'RE TRYING TO BE MICHAEL JORDAN! IT'S NOT GONNA HAPPEN! YOU HAVE **NO** CHANCE!

MYSELF, I DON'T LIVE VICARIOUSLY THROUGH **OTHER** PEOPLE! I DON'T PATTERN MYSELF AFTER **ANYONE**!

SO YOU'RE TRYING TO BE LIKE... NOBODY.

EXACTLY.

YOU'RE SUCCEEDING.

NAB!

I NEED TO WORK ON MY TRASH TALK.

CAN YOU GO DO IT ON THE BENCH?

SIIIIIGH...

!

TIP!

WONK!

WAM!

BASKETBALL INJURY.

WOW.

FRANCIS, THIS IS **RIDICULOUS**!

WHAT'S **RIDIC-ULOUS**?

TURNING YOUR DUMB **CAT** INTO A **MASCOT**!

WHAT'S SO **RIDICULOUS** ABOUT IT?

SHE'S A **CAT**, THAT'S WHAT! SHE'S A **HOUSE PET**! YOU CAN'T HAVE A **CAT** AS A **MASCOT**! IT MAKES A **MOCKERY** OF THE WHOLE IDEA OF MASCOTRY!

"MASCOTRY"?

A **REAL** MASCOT IS A GUY WEARING A FOAM RUBBER COSTUME.

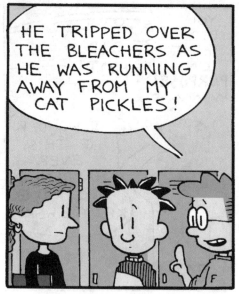

WHAT'S WRONG WITH MY TRASH-TALKING?? A KID JUST BUSTED ON ME, AND THE ONLY COMEBACK I COULD THINK OF WAS... "OH, **YEAH**?"

MY MIND IS A **BLANK** OUT THERE!

BUT AT LEAST YOU CAN STILL **PLAY**, RIGHT?

I CAN'T PLAY BALL WITHOUT TALKING SMACK! THAT'S LIKE SAMSON WITHOUT HIS HAIR! POPEYE WITHOUT HIS SPINACH! MOE AND LARRY WITHOUT CURLY!

SOONER OR LATER, IT ALWAYS COMES BACK TO THE THREE STOOGES.

I LIKE SHEMP!

BEING IN A TRASH-TALKING SLUMP IS A FEELING OF TOTAL **HELPLESSNESS!**

I MEAN, WHEN I'M OUT ON THE COURT, TALKING SMACK IS ONE OF THE THINGS THAT MAKES ME AN UNSTOPPABLE FORCE!

BUT NOW ANY **NIMROD** CAN BUST MY CHOPS, AND I JUST HAVE TO STAND THERE AND **TAKE** IT!

DID YOU ACTUALLY JUST REFER TO YOURSELF AS AN "UNSTOPPABLE FORCE"?

NOW DON'T **YOU** START!

...AND REMEMBER WHAT WE WORKED ON IN PRACTICE, GUYS! WE'LL NEED TO PLAY OUR BEST TO BEAT THIS TEAM!

PATIENT ON OFFENSE, TOUGH ON DEFENSE, RIGHT? OK, MEN, LET'S HIT THE FLOOR! LET'S GO GET 'EM!

AND MIGHT I ADD: BOZO THE CLOWN JUST CALLED. HE WANTS HIS TIE BACK.

I BEG YOUR PARDON?

JUST RAMPING UP MY TRASH TALK, COACH. GO, TEAM!

NATE, KEEP YOUR LIPS ZIPPED OUT THERE TODAY.

HM?

NO TRASH TALKING.

WHAT? BUT TRASH TALKING'S PART OF MY GAME! IT GIVES ME AN EDGE!

IF I CAN'T TALK SMACK OUT ON THE FLOOR, WHAT AM I SUPPOSED TO DO?

"PLAY DEFENSE." HARDY HAR HAR.

COACH! GOOD ONE!

NATE, THE GAME'S ABOUT TO START! WHAT ON EARTH ARE YOU DOING?

JUST MAKING SOME CARDS, COACH.

YOU WON'T LET ME TRASH-TALK, SO DURING THE GAME I'M GOING TO HAND OUT SOME OF **THESE**!

"IS THAT YOUR MOM OVER THERE, OR HAS GOODYEAR COME OUT WITH A FLESH-COLORED BLIMP?"

⁂ CHORTLE! ⁂ THAT'S A GOODY!

RRRIP!

I'M IN THE ZONE TODAY! I'M IN THE ZONE!

WHERE'S THE ZONE?

IT'S NOT A PLACE! IT'S MORE LIKE A **FEELING**!

IT'S THE FEELING YOU CAN DO NO WRONG! LIKE, IN BASKETBALL, IT'S THE FEELING YOU CAN'T MISS A SHOT!

...AND YOU REALLY **CAN'T** MISS! NOT WHEN YOU'RE IN THE ZONE!

HOW DO YOU GET IN THE ZONE?

IT JUST **HAPPENS**! ALL OF A SUDDEN IT'S JUST **THERE**!

FOO!

THUD!

OW!

...AND THEN, JUST AS SUDDENLY, IT'S GONE.

WHO THREW THAT?

COACH

44

THE NEWSPAPER DIDN'T PICK **ANY** OF OUR PLAYERS FOR THE PRESEASON ALL-STAR TEAM! **HA!** THANKS FOR THE **MOTIVATION!**

THEY'VE MADE US MAD! THEY'VE WOKEN UP THE **BEAST!**

WHO ARE YOU CALLING A BEAST?

W-WHAT, CHESTER?

YOU CALLED ME A BEAST. THAT MAKES ME WANT TO HIT YOU.

NO, I... ✳KOFF!✳ I SAID **BEETS!** I'M PRO-VEGETABLE!

NOW I WANT TO HIT YOU MORE THAN ONCE.

Peirce

OKAY, GANG, WE'VE BEEN PRACTICING FOR TWO WEEKS, AND IT'S ALL BEEN LEADING UP TO **THIS**: OUR **FIRST GAME!**

UNFORTUNATELY, WE'RE PLAYING THE BEST TEAM IN THE STATE AND THEY'RE UNBEATEN IN SIX YEARS... BUT IT'LL BE A **GREAT** TEST FOR US!

TRY YOUR HARDEST, DO YOUR BEST... AND DON'T GET DISCOURAGED. KEEP YOUR HEADS UP, NO MATTER WHAT HAPPENS.

MY ADRENAL GLANDS JUST COMPLETELY SHUT DOWN.

...AND HAVE **FUN** OUT THERE!

NATE, I'D LIKE YOU TO WORK ON YOUR LEFT HAND!

HM?

A GOOD POINT GUARD NEEDS TO DRIBBLE, SHOOT AND PASS WITH **EITHER** HAND!

COACH

ARRGH! I CAN'T DO **ANY**THING LEFTY! I KEEP WANTING TO USE MY **RIGHT** HAND!

I'VE GOT AN IDEA!

DRIBBA DRIB DRUB DRUB...

7

DUCT TAPE?

YUP! WE'LL TAPE YOUR RIGHT ARM!

THIS WAY YOU'LL **HAVE** TO USE YOUR LEFT HAND!

SHHK!

OKAY, OKAY. ISN'T THAT ENOUGH?

NOT YET. WE'VE GOTTA MAKE IT HOLD!

7

TWO MINUTES LATER...

I... WILL... KILL... YOU.

CATCH!

Peirce

51

COACH, REMEMBER LAST WEEK WHEN YOU TOLD ME TO WORK ON MY LEFT HAND?

WELL, I'VE BEEN PRACTICING! CHECK IT OUT!

DRIBBA DRIBBA

DRIBBLE DRIBBLE ⁂DRUB!⁂ OOPS!
BOUNCE KICK BOUNCE BONK
HEY! SORRY. DRIBBA DRIBBA
DRIB... THUD! OW! BOUNCE BOUNCE
CLANG! DRIBBLE HEADS UP!
DRIB DRIBDRIBDRIB.... DOOF! BOING!
⁂WONK!⁂ DANG! DRIBBLE DRUB...

WELL?
WHOOPS.

NATE, I CAN HONESTLY SAY THAT YOU ARE NOW EVERY BIT AS ACCOMPLISHED **LEFTY** AS YOU ARE RIGHTY.

WOW!

WAS THAT WHAT THEY CALL A "LEFT-HANDED COMPLIMENT"?

RIGHT.

OOPS.

Peirce

FIRST GAME OF THE SEASON, CHESTER! ARE YOU READY? ARE YOU PSYCHED? ARE YOU PUMPED?

WE CAN **BEAT** THIS TEAM! IF WE PLAY TOUGH DEFENSE AND REBOUND, WE SHOULD...

YOU'RE ANNOYING ME.

STOP ANNOYING ME, OR I'LL RIP YOUR ARM OFF AND BEAT YOU WITH IT.

FOR FUTURE REFERENCE, DON'T TALK TO CHESTER DURING HIS PRE-GAME BACK SHAVE.

Peirce

COACH, CAN WE GET A NEW MASCOT?

YOU DON'T LIKE "BOBCATS"?

BOBCATS IS FINE, BUT ON OUR **JERSEYS** IT'S SHORTENED TO "**CATS**"! IT MAKES US SOUND LIKE A BUNCH OF **HOUSE PETS!**

PLUS, I **HATE** CATS! I'M A **DOG** PERSON!

BUT "CATS" IS THE NAME OF MY FAVORITE MUSICAL!

I WONDER IF RED AUERBACH EVER HAD TIME-OUTS LIKE THIS.

DON'T START SINGING, CHAD.

Peirce

58

WHAT'S WITH THE BLACK SOCKS?

I HAD NO CHOICE. MY **LUCKY** SOCKS HAVE **DISAPPEARED**!

HEH HEH!... YOU LOOK LIKE ONE OF THOSE OLD GUYS WHO WEARS BLACK SOCKS UNDER HIS SANDALS!

YOU SHOULD BE "POWER WALKING" AROUND THE MALL!

MY FAVORITE PLACE IN THE MALL IS "PRETZEL TIME"!

IT ALWAYS COMES BACK TO THE FOOD COURT.

WE'RE TALKING ABOUT SOCKS, CHAD.

I ALSO LIKE "ORANGE JULIUS"!

WHAT A LOUSY PRACTICE.

WE'D BETTER SHAPE UP BEFORE WE PLAY JEFFERSON.

IF I DON'T FIND MY LUCKY SOCKS, WE HAVE NO CHANCE.

JUST GET YOURSELF SOME **NEW** LUCKY SOCKS!

HEY, WHAT A GREAT **IDEA**, TEDDY! WHY DIDN'T **I** THINK OF THAT?

HELLO, **ROOM SERVICE?** SEND UP A PAIR OF ONE-OF-A-KIND **LUCKY SOCKS,** PLEASE!

HOW CAN A PAIR BE ONE-OF-A-KIND?

⁎SIGH⁎

SO WHERE DO YOU THINK YOU LOST YOUR LUCKY SOCKS?

I DIDN'T **LOSE** THEM, FRANCIS!

I LEFT THEM IN MY LOCKER AFTER PRACTICE YESTERDAY, AND TODAY THEY WERE **GONE**! WHICH MEANS SOMEONE **STOLE** THEM!

SOLVING THIS CASE WILL REQUIRE INVESTIGATIVE EXPERTISE, UNERRING INSTINCTS, AND AWE-INSPIRING BRAIN POWER!

GOT ANYBODY IN MIND?

LOSE THE SARCASM, FRANCIS, AND I **MIGHT** LET YOU BE MY TRUSTY ASSISTANT.

HELLO, NATE! READY FOR ANOTHER GREAT BASEBALL SEASON?

THAT DEPENDS.

IS OUR TEAM STILL GONNA BE CALLED "JOE'S TACOS"? THAT STUPID NAME WAS SO.... HEY, **WAIT** A MINUTE! WHAT'S **THAT?**

WHAT'S WHAT?

ON YOUR HAT! "CL"! WE HAVE A NEW NAME, DON'T WE? WHAT DOES "CL" STAND FOR?

"CHEZ LINDA"

OKAY, GANG, BRING IT IN!!

WHAT? WHOA! **HEY!** **WHAT??**

66

LOOK, GANG, I KNOW YOU'RE NOT HAPPY TO BE PLAYING ON A TEAM CALLED "CHEZ LINDA", BUT IT'S JUST A **NAME**!

WHAT **REALLY** MATTERS IS PLAYING HARD AND TO THE BEST OF YOUR ABILITY! AND YOU GUYS HAVE A **LOT** OF ABILITY!

PLAY LIKE YOU'RE CAPABLE AND YOU'LL MAKE "CHEZ LINDA" THE MOST **FEARED** NAME IN THE ENTIRE **LEAGUE**!

THEY'RE NOT BUYING THIS.

LISTEN TO YOURSELF, MAN.

DAD! WHERE'S MY BASEBALL UNIFORM?

IT'S BAD ENOUGH I PLAY FOR A TEAM CALLED "CHEZ LINDA"!... I DON'T WANT TO BE LATE FOR MY FIRST GAME **TOO**!

I... ER... I WASHED IT.

OH!... THANKS, DAD.

WELL... DON'T THANK ME YET...

WHY ARE YOU HIDING IT BEHIND YOUR BACK?

Peirce

IS THAT MY BASE-BALL UNIFORM BEHIND YOUR BACK?

ER... YES.

I THOUGHT I'D WASH IT, SO YOU'D LOOK SHARP FOR YOUR FIRST GAME OF THE SEASON...

BUT... ✻AHEM!✻... SOMEHOW MY RED SWEAT-SHIRT GOT MIXED IN WITH THE WHITES, AND...

IT'S PINK!

WELL, TECH-NICALLY, I'D CALL IT MORE OF A "SALMON."

HEY! LOOK AT YOUR...

HEE HEE

I KNOW, I KNOW! MY UNIFORM IS **PINK**!

MY DAD TRIED TO WASH IT AND TOTALLY MESSED IT UP! IT'S **PINK**, THERE'S **NOTHING** I CAN DO ABOUT IT, SO LET'S **MOVE ON**!

ACTUALLY, THAT'S MORE LIKE "SALMON."

WHATEVER. CAN WE CHANGE THE SUBJECT?

IT'S YOUR **FACE** THAT'S **PINK**!

ALL RIGHT ALREADY!

WELL, WELL! LOOK WHO IT **IS**, GUYS! THE RIGHT FIELDER FOR "CHEZ LINDA"!

READY FOR TODAY'S GAME, BIG FELLA? IT SURE **SEEMS** LIKE YOU ARE! YOU LOOK STRONG! YOU LOOK HEALTHY!

ONE MIGHT SAY YOU'RE "IN THE **PINK**"!

WA HA HA HA A HA HA HA HA HA HA HA HA HA OH, MAN! GOOD ONE, KEVIN! HA HA HA

Peirce

79

IT'S A BEAUTIFUL DAY, NATE! TIME FOR A GAME OF CATCH!

GROAN..

OH, COME ON! IT'S A GREAT WAY TO GET EXERCISE!

IT'S MORE EXERCISE FOR SOME OF US THAN OTHERS.

SORRY!

82

sigh...

CAN'T FIND IT, DAD! LOOKS LIKE THAT BALL'S HISTORY!

OH, WELL! GUESS WE CAN'T PLAY CATCH ANYMORE!

THERE IT IS!

GREAT.

THAT'S THE PROBLEM WITH YOU KIDS! YOU **GIVE UP** TOO EASILY!

OKAY, SO I PLAY FOR A TEAM CALLED "CHEEZ LINDA"! SO **WHAT**? THERE'S A **GAME** TO PLAY! A **BIG** GAME! AN **IMPORTANT** GAME!

CRACK!

HEY! **SWISS CHEEZ LINDA!**

A LONG GAME.

WA HA HA HA HA HA HA HA HA HA GOOD ONE, LYLE! HA HA HA HA HA

✳ sigh...✳

KRAK!

YES!

BAG OF CHIPS AND AN ORANGE SODA, PLEASE.

THE MOST EXCITING PLAY IN BASEBALL:

A FOUL BALL THAT LANDS NEAR THE SNACK BOOTH!

Peirce

MAN! IT'S **BOILING** OUT HERE!

WHAT WAS I **THINKING**, WEARING A **LONG-SLEEVE** UNDERSHIRT?

I'VE GOT TO GET THIS THING OFF BEFORE I GET **HEAT STROKE!**

BUT **HOW**? I CAN'T STRIP TO THE WAIST IN THE MIDDLE OF **RIGHT FIELD!**

WAIT! I'LL BET I CAN GET OUT OF THE UNDERSHIRT **WITHOUT** TAKING OFF MY **UNIFORM!**

JUST GOTTA GET MY ARMS INSIDE HERE...

NOW GET MY HANDS FREE...

...AND PULL THIS OUT...

YES! DID IT!

THUD!

WONDER WHAT COACH IS YELLING ABOUT.

SPRING TRAINING

LITTLE LEAGUE ROSTERS TODAY ⚾ PICK UP UNIFORMS HERE

HI, COACH!

WELL! HELLO, GENTS! READY FOR ANOTHER GREAT SEASON?

T·BALL
DOUBLE A
MAJORS

UH... THAT DEPENDS ON OUR TEAM NAME.

YEAH, WHO'S OUR SPONSOR?

...BECAUSE LAST YEAR WE PLAYED FOR A BEAUTY PARLOR! AND IT WAS MISSPELLED ON OUR UNIFORMS!

YEAH! "CHEEZ LINDA"! WE WERE A LAUGHING-STOCK!

NOT TO WORRY, BOYS! "CHEEZ LINDA" IS NO MORE!

REALLY?

WE HAVE A NEW SPONSOR?

WE CERTAINLY DO! AND THE NAME ISN'T MISSPELLED, EITHER!

Peirce

...UNFORTUNATELY.

NO!... NO!

CONTINUED NEXT WEEK!!

KRAK!

HOME! HOME!! PLAY AT THE PLATE!

WUMP!

HOLY SMOKES! THIS GUY'S COMIN' FAST!...AND HE'S HUGE!

I'M GONNA GET FLATTENED LIKE A PANCAKE!

AND FOR WHAT? TO PREVENT A RUN IN A LITTLE LEAGUE GAME WE'RE ALREADY LOSING TEN-ZIP? IS IT REALLY WORTH IT?

I DON'T THINK SO.

SAFE!

HEY, STAN! YOU FORGOT TO WIPE YOUR FEET!

HA HA HA HA HA HA

PLAYING FOR THE "DOORMATS" IS BECOMING A SELF-FULFILLING PROPHECY.

98

MAN, COACH JOHN IS SUCH A PSYCHO.

NO, HE'S NOT! I'LL BET IT'S ALL AN ACT!

HE ACTS ALL PSYCHO ON THE **OUT**SIDE, BUT ON THE **IN**SIDE, HE'S PROBABLY JUST A SOFT, FLUFFY MARSHMALLOW!

NO CHIT-CHAT, SOLDIERS! GIVE ME TWENTY! NOW!!

EVER TRY TO EAT A MARSHMALLOW AFTER SOMEBODY DROPPED IT IN THE SAND?

COACH! WE JUST HEARD THEY'RE CONTRACTING THE LITTLE LEAGUE!

YUP. I'M ON MY WAY TO THE DISPERSAL DRAFT.

COAC

DISPERSAL DRAFT?

THE TEAMS THAT ARE **LEFT** DRAFT PLAYERS FROM THE TEAMS THAT **FOLDED**.

OACH

AND THESE ARE THE KIDS THAT ARE AVAILABLE?

RIGHT!

IN A WORD: YIKES

DID YOU SAY DISPERSAL DRAFT OR DISPOSAL DRAFT?

Peirce

COACH! OUR JERSEYS DON'T HAVE A **NAME** ON 'EM!

WE **HAVE** NO NAME!

THAT'S ONE REASON THE LEAGUE CONTRACTED! WE'VE LOST SOME OF OUR SPONSORS!

SO WHO **ARE** WE, THEN?

I GUESS WE'RE... THE NOTHINGS!

"LET'S GO, NOTHINGS"?

I'M PINING FOR THE GOOD OL' DAYS OF "LET'S GO, CHEZ LINDA."

BOYS, I THINK OUR TEAM CAN GO PLACES THIS YEAR! MAYBE ALL THE WAY TO THE **LITTLE LEAGUE WORLD SERIES!**

THE TEAMS THAT GO TO THE SERIES ALWAYS HAVE A GUY WHO LOOKS LIKE A STEROID-PUMPED **FREAKAZOID!** WELL, NOW **WE'VE** GOT ONE, **TOO!**

CHESTER, **YOU** ARE **OUR** FREAKAZOID!

IF WE WANT TO GET TO THE LITTLE LEAGUE WORLD SERIES, WE'LL HAVE TO WORK ON OUR TEAM CHEMISTRY.

Peirce

Crack!

SHUMPF!

ARRGH! A GOPHER HOLE!

I CAN'T MOVE!

NATE! CATCH IT!

WAP!

YES! WHAT A GRAB!

HE'S TAGGIN' UP!

BASEBALL IS A CRUEL GAME.

ALL RIGHT, BOYS... WE'RE A BIT SHORT-HANDED TODAY. IN FACT, WE'VE ONLY GOT NINE PLAYERS.

COACH

THAT MEANS THAT EACH OF YOU WILL HAVE TO PLAY THE WHOLE GAME! EVEN THOSE OF YOU WHO HAVEN'T PLAYED MUCH THIS YEAR!

IF WE WANT TO WIN THE CHAMPIONSHIP, ALL OF YOU WILL HAVE TO STEP UP AND PLAY MISTAKE-FREE BALL!

THAT MEANS YOU, CHAD.

ME?

IT'S HERO TIME, MAN.

WHAT DO YOU GUYS THINK YOU'RE DOING?

WHAT ARE WE DOING? WE'RE **BEATING YOU BY FIFTEEN RUNS!**

EX**ACT**LY! SO HOW COME YOU'RE STILL BUNTING AND STEALING BASES?

BECAUSE... ...WELL... BECAUSE THAT'S HOW YOU **WIN.**

BILLY!! STOP FRATERNIZING WITH THE ENEMY!!

...AND BECAUSE YOUR COACH IS A PSYCHO.

SSSH!

✳SNICKER!✳ WE'RE DE**STROY**ING YOU GUYS!

YEAH?

WELL, **IF** WE WEREN'T MISSING OUR BEST PITCHER, AND **IF** OUR BEST HITTER WASN'T ON A CAMPING TRIP, AND **IF** TEDDY HADN'T JUST THROWN THE BALL OVER THE BACKSTOP...

...AND **IF** CHAD HADN'T COMMITTED THOSE FIVE ERRORS IN THE FIRST INNING, AND **IF** I'D REMEMBERED TO WEAR MY LUCKY SOCKS, THEN **WE** WOULD BE DE-STROYING **YOU** GUYS!

RIGHT.

"HYPOTHETICAL TRASH TALKING" IS KIND OF LAME, BUT SOMETIMES IT'S ALL YOU'VE GOT.

WHAT HAVE WE LEARNED HERE, COACH?

WHAT DO YOU MEAN, NATE?

COACH

OUR TEAM PLAYED AS HARD AS WE COULD, WE TREATED OUR OPPONENTS WITH RESPECT, WE DIDN'T COMPLAIN ABOUT ANY BAD CALLS... AND WE **LOST**!

THEIR TEAM RAN UP THE SCORE, SCREAMED AT THE UMP, TALKED TRASH ALL GAME, SHOWBOATED EVERY TIME THEY SCORED... AND THEY **WON**!

...TWENTY-EIGHT TO THREE.

YEAH. WHAT HAVE WE LEARNED HERE?

THINK FAST, COACH.

COACH

Peirce

145

CRACK!

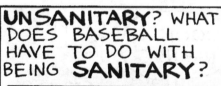

KLONK!

NICE HIT, NICK.

THANKS. IT STUNG, THOUGH.

I FEEL LIKE I'M HOLDING A HANDFUL OF BEES.

HEY, I'VE GOT A GOOD REMEDY FOR THAT!

YOU'VE GOT TO GET THE BLOOD MOVING BACK INTO YOUR HANDS! DO A FEW QUICK PUSH-UPS!

PUSH-UPS?

THERE YOU GO! THAT'LL DO THE TRICK!

YER OUT!

TAG!

...THE KEY WORD BEING "TRICK"!

THAT STUNG.

155

MY BAT'S **STILL** TOO SLOW! **THIS** TIME, I'LL START MY SWING AS SOON AS HE GOES INTO HIS WIND-UP!..... **NOW!**

HE WAS ONLY SCRATCHING HIS NOSE.

STRIKE TWO.

GOAL!

WRIGHT!

YIP!

WHAT'S THE HOLD-UP HERE? THE SCRIMMAGE IS STARTING! EVERYBODY'S WAITING!!

I CAN'T FIND MY MOUTHGUARD.

AGAIN? WHAT'S THAT, THE TENTH TIME TODAY?

IT WAS HERE A SECOND AGO.

IS THIS IT?

YEAH! YEAH, THAT'S IT!

WELL, DON'T JUST STAND THERE! PUT IT IN!!

NMPH!

NOW GET OUT THERE!! TIME'S A-WASTING! GO! GO! GO!

WUMP!

PTOO!

? ? ?

I CAN'T FIND MY MOUTHGUARD.

A GOOD GOALIE MUST HAVE CAT-LIKE REFLEXES!

I'M A CAT! I'M A CAT!

WAIT A MINUTE! I DON'T WANT TO BE A CAT! I HATE CATS!

I'LL BE A CHEETAH! A CHEETAH'S QUICK!

HOLD IT! A CHEETAH IS JUST AN OVERGROWN CAT!!

I'M A COBRA! THAT'S IT! I'M A COBRA!

NO, A COBRA SOUNDS TOO SLIMY! I CAN'T BE A COBRA!

A SHARK?

NO, TOO AQUATIC.

A GAZELLE?

NOT RUGGED ENOUGH.

A HORSE?... NO. AN EAGLE? NO. WHAT SHOULD I BE?

A GOAT.

Peirce

165

166

HEY, **HEY**! WHAT ARE YOU **DOING**?

YOU'RE NOT SUPPOSED TO TRY TO **SCORE** DURING **WARM-UPS**, FRANCIS YOU IDIOT! THE POINT IS TO **LOOSEN UP THE GOALIE**!

THIS TIME, SHOOT IT RIGHT **AT** ME!

CAN I HAVE AN ICE PACK?

COACH

Peirce

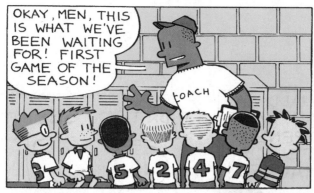

YOU'RE SO **TRANS-PARENT**, NATE!

YEAH, YOU'RE SO **OBVIOUSLY** JEALOUS OF ARTUR!

JEALOUS?

I'M NOT **JEALOUS** OF ARTUR! I JUST DON'T **LIKE** THE KID, THAT'S ALL! HE'S MY **ARCH-ENEMY**!

I THOUGHT **MRS. GODFREY** WAS YOUR ARCH-ENEMY!

SHE **IS**! SHE **AND** ARTUR!

LIKE SUPERMAN, I HAVE **MANY** ARCH-ENEMIES!

HE'S COMPARING HIMSELF TO AN IMMORTAL BEING.

AGAIN?

OKAY, MAYBE I **AM** A LITTLE JEALOUS OF ARTUR! **I** WAS THE BEST CHESS PLAYER IN SCHOOL AND THEN **HE** CAME ALONG! **I** WAS THE BEST ARTIST AND THEN **HE** CAME ALONG!

...AND NOW IT'S GOING TO HAPPEN **AGAIN!** HE'S GOING TO BREEZE IN AND STEAL MY PLACE AS THE STAR OF THE SOCCER TEAM!

NATE, NATE, NATE...

YOU'RE NOT THE STAR OF THE SOCCER TEAM.

BUT IT'S CUTE THAT YOU THINK SO!

PAT PAT

LET'S **GO**, BOYS! PRACTICE STARTS **FIVE MINUTES AGO**!

WHAT ARE YOU DOING?

SSHH!

COACH

I'M WATCHING ARTUR GET DRESSED FOR PRACTICE.

WHAT FOR?

TO SEE IF HE'S ANY **GOOD**, OF COURSE!

EVERYONE KNOWS YOU CAN PREDICT SOMEBODY'S LEVEL OF ATHLETIC SKILL BY WATCHING THE WAY HE GETS DRESSED BEFOREHAND!

...SAID THE GOALIE WITH HIS SHORTS ON BACKWARD.

HE'S TAPING HIS ANKLES.

HE MUST BE GOOD.

WELL, WELL, WELL! THE BIG GAME AGAINST JEFFERSON IS TOMORROW, AND **ARTUR** IS STARTING AT HALFBACK! AND HE CAN'T EVEN PLAY!

LOOKS LIKE MISTER "I'M GOOD AT EVERYTHING" CAN'T BE A HERO **THIS** TIME! JEFFERSON'S GOING TO CRUSH US LIKE A BAG OF ICE! THIS IS **GREAT**!

UH... I MEAN... GREAT**LY**!...

GREATLY DISTRESSING! THIS IS **GREATLY DISTRESSING**!

WEDGIE?

WEDGIE.

NATE? YOU HEADING HOME? I'VE GOT TO GET GOING!

※SIGH※

COACH

GREAT GAME, WASN'T IT?

OH, SURE! IF YOUR NAME IS **ARTUR** IT WAS A GREAT GAME!

COACH

HE **STINKS** AT SOCCER, AND YET HE STILL FINDS A WAY TO SCORE THE **WINNING GOAL!** HE IS SO **LUCKY!** HE IS THE **LUCKIEST** KID I'VE EVER **SEEN!**

ON SECOND THOUGHT, I MAY BE HERE AWHILE.

"HEY, ARTUR, WHAT'S THAT STUCK TO YOUR SHOE? WHY, IT'S A **HUNDRED DOLLAR BILL!**"

COACH

TIME! GAME OVER, GENTS!

HONK

WHAT'S WITH YOU?

WHATTA YA MEAN?

WHY DO YOU LOOK SO **MAD**?

WE **WON**!

I KNOW.

BUT I'VE STILL GOT MY **GAME FACE** ON!

I SPENT ALL **DAY** GETTING PSYCHED UP FOR THIS GAME! I **WILLED** MY FACE INTO A MASK OF COMPETITIVE INTENSITY!

I CAN'T JUST **TURN OFF** THAT INTENSITY LIKE A...

HEL**LO**, LADIES!

...LIKE A HOSE.

LOTS OF PEOPLE HERE TODAY. THIS IS THE BIGGEST CROWD WE'VE HAD ALL YEAR!

WELL, THEY'RE NOT GONNA SEE ANYONE SCORE ON **ME**, I'LL GUARANT—...✳

OOP! LOOK WHO'S HERE! **JENNY!**

...AND LOOK WHO **ELSE! GREG PROXMIRE!** HER **MAIN SQUEEZE!**

I CAN'T **BELIEVE** THEY'RE STILL AN ITEM! THE QUESTION IS: **WHY?**

I MEAN, WHAT'S THE APPEAL? HE'S A **STIFF!** SHE COULD DO SO MUCH BETTER!

LIKE **ME**, FOR INSTANCE! DOESN'T SHE REALIZE I'M **PERFECT** FOR HER? DOESN'T SHE...

✳AHEM!✳

WHAT'S YOUR PROBLEM?

MY PROBLEM? **GREG PROXMIRE**, THAT'S MY PROBLEM!

WHAT'S **HE** GOT THAT **I** HAVEN'T GOT?

WELL, FOR ONE THING, HE'S MORE OBSERVANT.

IN WHAT WAY?

CRIPES.

197

WHOA, ARTUR, **WHOA**! WHAT'S GOING ON HERE?

AM TRY-ING OUT FOR TEAM!

BUT YOU TRIED THAT **LAST** YEAR, REMEMBER? AND YOU FOUND OUT YOU **STINK** AT SOCCER!

YES! WHEN I TRY TO **SCORE** THE BALL, I STINK!

SO COACH MADE SUGGESTION FOR ME TO INSTEAD TRY TO **SAVING** BALL!

COACH DID?

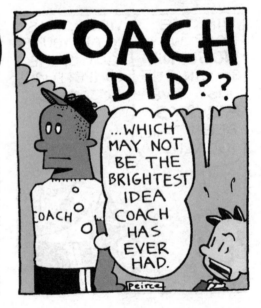

COACH DID??

...WHICH MAY NOT BE THE BRIGHTEST IDEA COACH HAS EVER HAD.

COACH

Peirce

COACH! HOW COME YOU TOLD **ARTUR** HE COULD TRY OUT FOR **GOALIE**?

WELL, WHY **SHOULDN'T** HE?

BECAUSE **I'M** OUR GOALIE!

YES! AND YOU'RE AN **EXCELLENT** ONE!

...WHICH IS WHY **ARTUR** PLAYING ALONGSIDE YOU IS SUCH A GOOD THING! HE HAS SO MUCH TO **LEARN** FROM YOU!

OH. UH... RIGHT!

BEFORE I SWITCHED TO PHYS. ED., I WAS A PSYCH MAJOR.

Peirce

OKAY, ARTUR, WATCH CAREFULLY! FOR A GOALIE, THE MOST IMPORTANT THING IS TO HAVE A GOOD **WARM-UP!**

OKAY, GUYS, WARM ME UP!

DOOF!

I AM CONFUSED. HOW YOU TO GET WARM WITH COLD ICE ON FACE?

SHUT UP, ARTUR.

I NEED A NICK-NAME.

YEAH?

YEAH! OUR FORWARDS CALL THEMSELVES "STRIKE FORCE"! OUR DEFENDERS ARE "THE BEEFY D"!

AS OUR GOALKEEPER, I HAVE NO IDENTITY! I NEED A NICKNAME!

HOW ABOUT "PINHEAD"?

A SOCCER NICK-NAME!

IT WORKS FOR SOCCER!

FRANCIS! TEDDY! I'VE COME UP WITH THE PERFECT SOCCER NICKNAME FOR MYSELF!

AS A GOALKEEPER, MY JOB IS TO LET IN ZERO GOALS! SO I'M CALLING MYSELF "MISTER ZERO"!

MISTER ZERO... I LIKE IT.

YEAH, THAT'S GOOD.

...BECAUSE YOU CAN APPLY IT TO SO **MANY** PARTS OF YOUR LIFE!

...LIKE DATING!

AWRIGHT, LADIES, YOU KNOW WHY YOU LOST YESTERDAY? YOU GOT **OUTMUSCLED**!!

TO WIN, YOU HAVE TO LEARN HOW TO PLAY AGAINST TEAMS THAT ARE **BIGGER** AND **STRONGER**!

...SO **TODAY** YOU'RE GOING TO PRACTICE AGAINST THE **8TH** GRADERS! **COME ON OVER, MEN**!

STOMP! STOMP! STOMP! STOMP!

"MEN" IS RIGHT.

IS IT TOO LATE TO SWITCH TO CROSS-COUNTRY?